EASIEST KEYBOARD COLLECTION

New Pop Hits

WISE PUBLICATIONS
London/New York/Paris/Sydney/Copenhagen/Berlin/Madrid/Tokyo

Exclusive Distributors:

Music Sales Limited
8/9 Frith Street,
London W1D 3JB, England.

Music Sales Pty Limited
120 Rothschild Avenue,
Rosebery, NSW 2018,
Australia.

Order No. AM976492
ISBN 0-7119-9828-0
This book © Copyright 2003 by Wise Publications

Compiled by Lucy Holliday
Music arranged by Roger Day
Music processed by Paul Ewers Music Design

Printed in the United Kingdom by
Caligraving Limited, Thetford, Norfolk.

Your Guarantee of Quality
As publishers, we strive to produce every book to the highest
commercial standards.
The music has been freshly engraved and the book has been carefully
designed to minimise awkward page turns and to make playing from
it a real pleasure.
Particular care has been given to specifying acid-free, neutral-sized
paper made from pulps which have not been elemental chlorine
bleached. This pulp is from farmed sustainable forests and was
produced with special regard for the environment.
Throughout, the printing and binding have been planned to ensure
a sturdy, attractive publication which should give years of enjoyment.
If your copy fails to meet our high standards, please inform us and
we will gladly replace it.

www.musicsales.com

Contents

ALL THE THINGS SHE SAID

Words & Music by Sergei Galoyan, Trevor Horn, Martin Kierszenbaum, Elena Kiper & Valerij Polienko

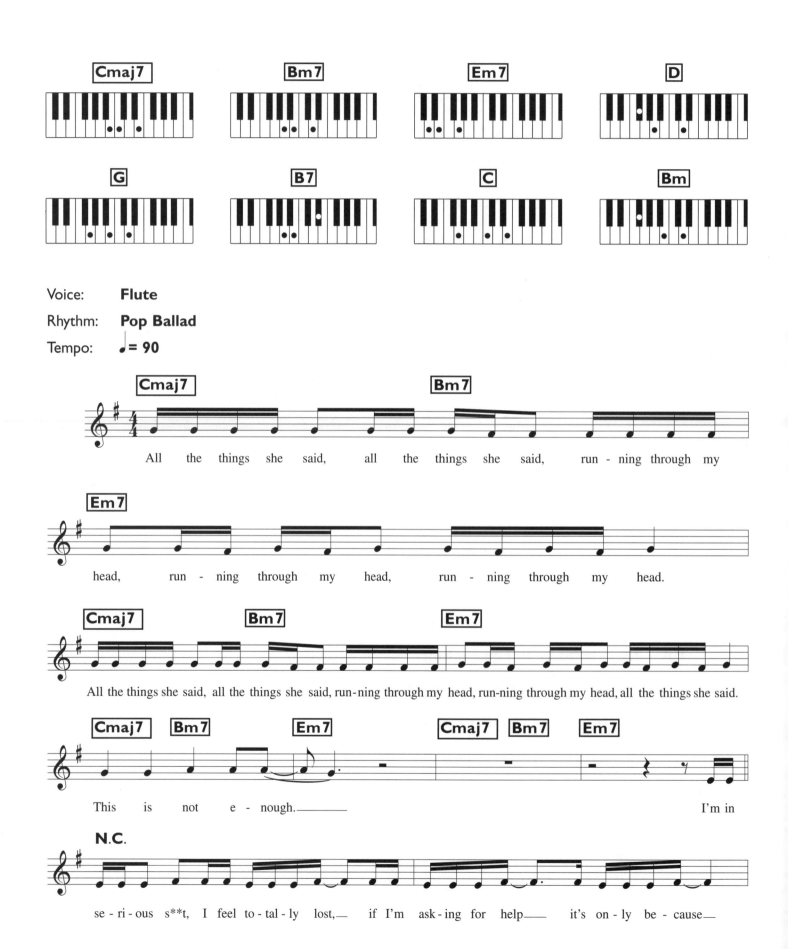

ANYONE OF US (STUPID MISTAKE)

Words & Music by Jörgen Elofsson, Per Magnusson & David Kreuger
© Copyright 2002 BMG Music Publishing Limited (50%)/
Good Ear Music/Peermusic (UK) Limited (25%)/Warner/Chappell Music Limited (25%).
All Rights Reserved. International Copyright Secured.

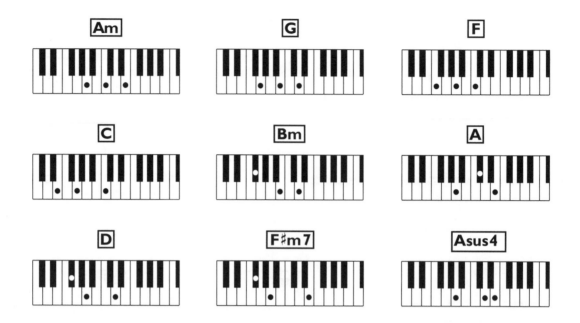

Voice: **Studio Piano**

Rhythm: **Dance Pop I**

Tempo: ♩ = 104

I've been let-ting you down, down,— girl I know I've been such a fool.—

Giv-ing in to temp-ta-tion,— I should-'ve played it cool.

The si-tu-a-tion got out of hand,— I hope you un-der-stand, it can hap-pen to

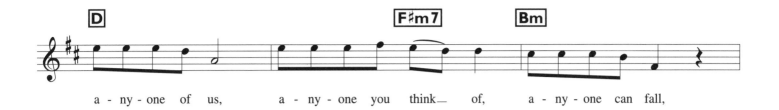

a - ny - one of us, a - ny - one you think— of, a - ny - one can fall,

a - ny - one can hurt some - one—— they love,—— hearts— will break— 'cause

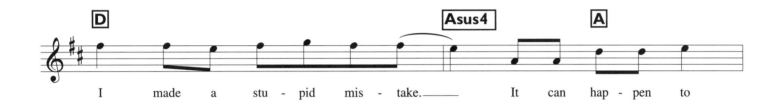

I made a stu - pid mis - take.—— It can hap - pen to

a - ny - one of us, say you will for - give me,

a - ny - one can fail, say you will be - lieve me, I——

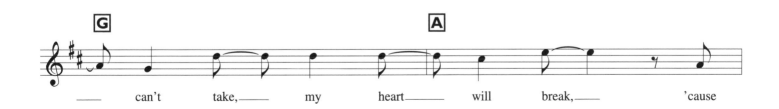

—— can't take,—— my heart—— will break,—— 'cause

I made a stu - pid mis - take,—— a stu - pid mis - take.——

BEAUTIFUL

Words & Music by Linda Perry

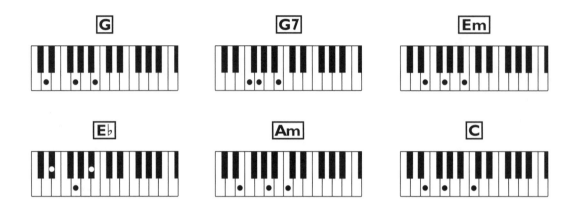

Voice: **Clarinet**

Rhythm: **Soul Ballad**

Tempo: ♩ = **76**

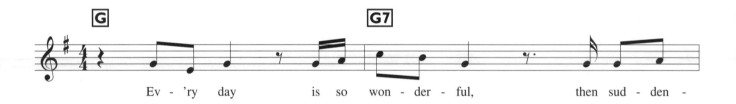

Ev - 'ry day   is   so   won - der - ful,   then sud - den -

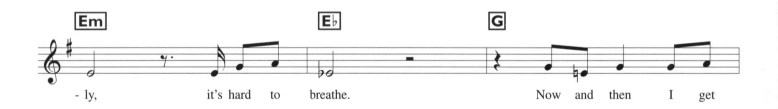

- ly,   it's   hard   to   breathe.   Now   and   then   I   get

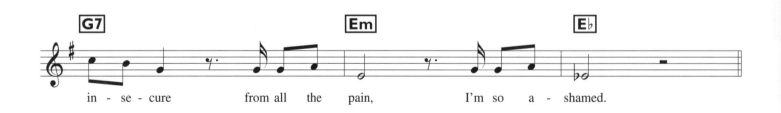

in - se - cure   from   all   the   pain,   I'm   so   a - shamed.

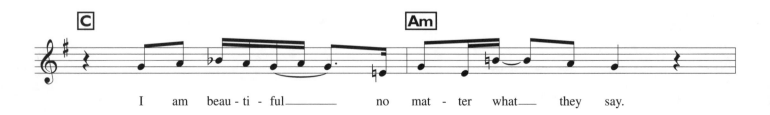

I   am   beau - ti - ful_____   no   mat - ter   what___   they   say.

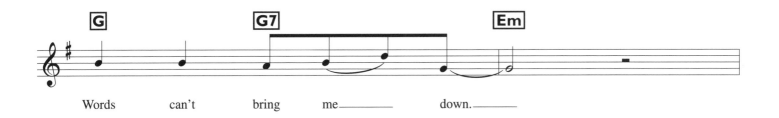

Words can't bring me down.

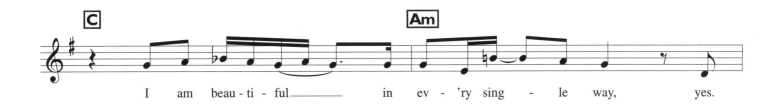

I am beau-ti-ful _____ in ev-'ry sing - le way, yes.

Words can't bring me _____ down, _____ oh no. _____

So don't you bring me down to - day.

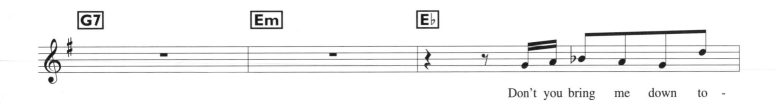

Don't you bring me down to -

- day,

don't you bring me down to - day.

THE CHEEKY SONG (TOUCH MY BUM)

Words & Music by Pete Kirtley, Timothy Hawes & Margit Semal

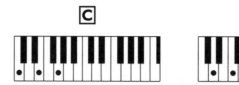

Voice: **Electric Piano 3**

Rhythm: **Dance Pop 1**

Tempo: ♩**= 126**

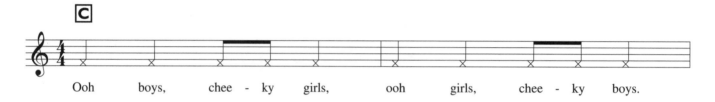

Ooh boys, chee - ky girls, ooh girls, chee - ky boys.

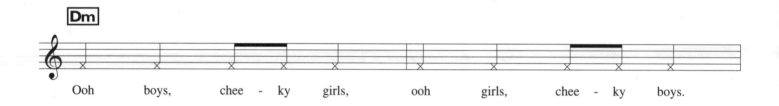

Ooh boys, chee - ky girls, ooh girls, chee - ky boys.

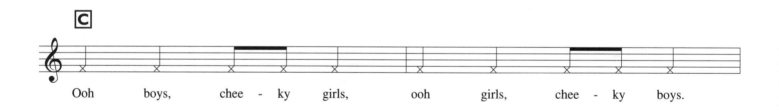

Ooh boys, chee - ky girls, ooh girls, chee - ky boys.

Ooh boys, chee - ky girls, ooh girls, chee - ky boys. I

nev - er ev - er ask where do you go, I

never ever ask   what do you do.   I   nev - er ev - er ask   what's

in   your   mind,   I   nev - er ev - er ask   if   you'll   be   mine.

Come   and— smile,   don't   be— shy.   Touch   my— bum,

this   is— life.

We   are   the chee - ky girls,   we   are   the chee - ky girls.   You   are   the chee - ky boys,

you   are   the chee - ky boys.   We   are   the chee - ky girls,   we   are   the chee - ky girls,

you   are   the chee - ky boys,   you   are   the chee - ky boys.   Chee - ky, chee - ky.

COLOURBLIND

Words & Music by Darius, Pete Glenister & Denny Lew

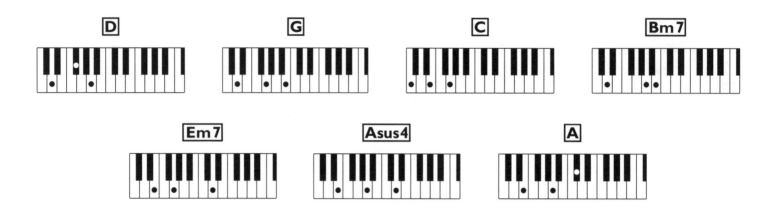

Voice: **Electric Piano 2**

Rhythm: **Dance Pop 2**

Tempo: ♩ = 108

Feel - in' blue____ when I'm tryin' to for-get the feel - in' that I____

____ miss____ you.____ Feel - in' green,____ when my

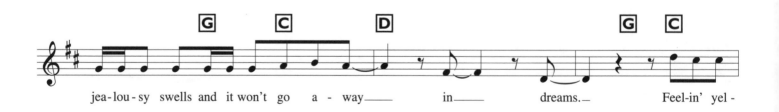

jea-lou-sy swells and it won't go a - way____ in____ dreams.____ Feel-in' yel-

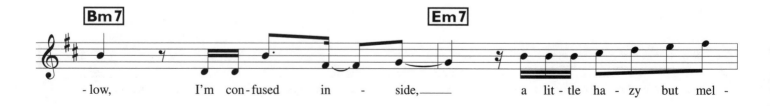

- low, I'm con-fused in - side,____ a lit-tle ha-zy but mel-

- low, then I feel your— eyes—— on me,— feel-in' fine,— sub - lime,— when that

smile of yours— creeps in - to my mind,—— oh oh.—

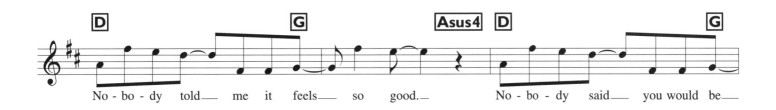

No - bo - dy told— me it feels— so good.— No - bo - dy said— you would be—

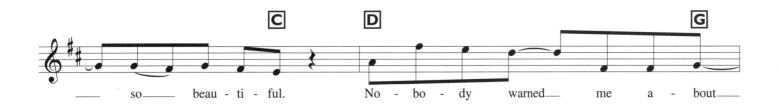

—— so— beau - ti - ful. No - bo - dy warned— me a - bout——

—— your smile,— you're the light,— you're the light— when I close my eyes..

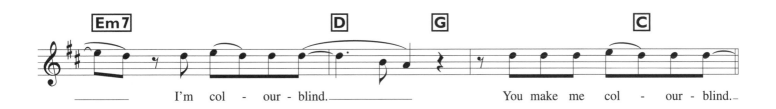

—— I'm col - our - blind.— You make me col - our - blind.

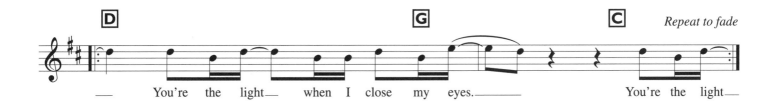

Repeat to fade

— You're the light— when I close my eyes.—— You're the light—

COME INTO MY WORLD

Words & Music by Cathy Dennis & Rob Davis
© Copyright 2001 EMI Music Publishing Limited (50%)/
Universal/MCA Music Limited (50%).

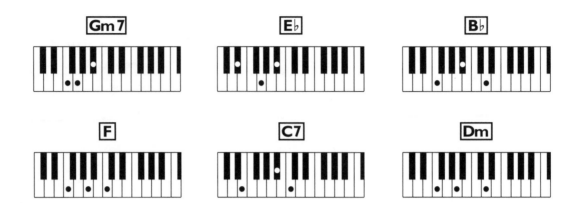

Voice: **Gut Guitar**

Rhythm: **Disco**

Tempo: ♩ = 124

Come, come, come in-to my world,

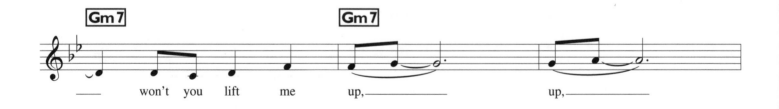

won't you lift me up, up,

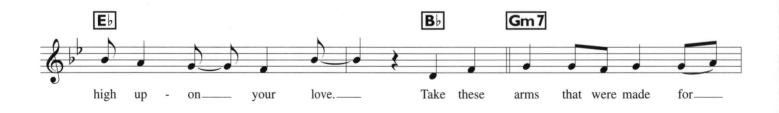

high up-on your love. Take these arms that were made for

lov-ing, and this heart that will beat for two. Take these

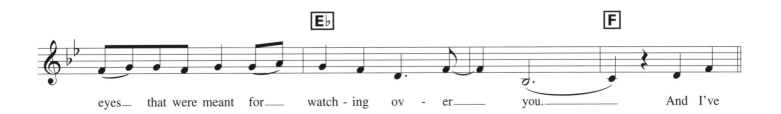

eyes— that were meant for— watch-ing ov - er— you.— And I've

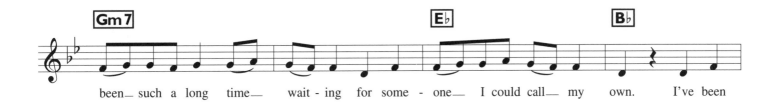

been— such a long time— wait-ing for some - one— I could call— my own. I've been

chas - ing the life I've— dreamed and now I'm— home.—

Ah,— I need— your— love—

like night— needs— morn - ing.—

Na na na na na na na na na na na na na na na.

Repeat to fade

Na na na na na na na na na na na na na na na.

GOT TO HAVE YOUR LOVE

Words & Music by Brice Wilson, Kirk Khaleel & Johnny Rodriguez

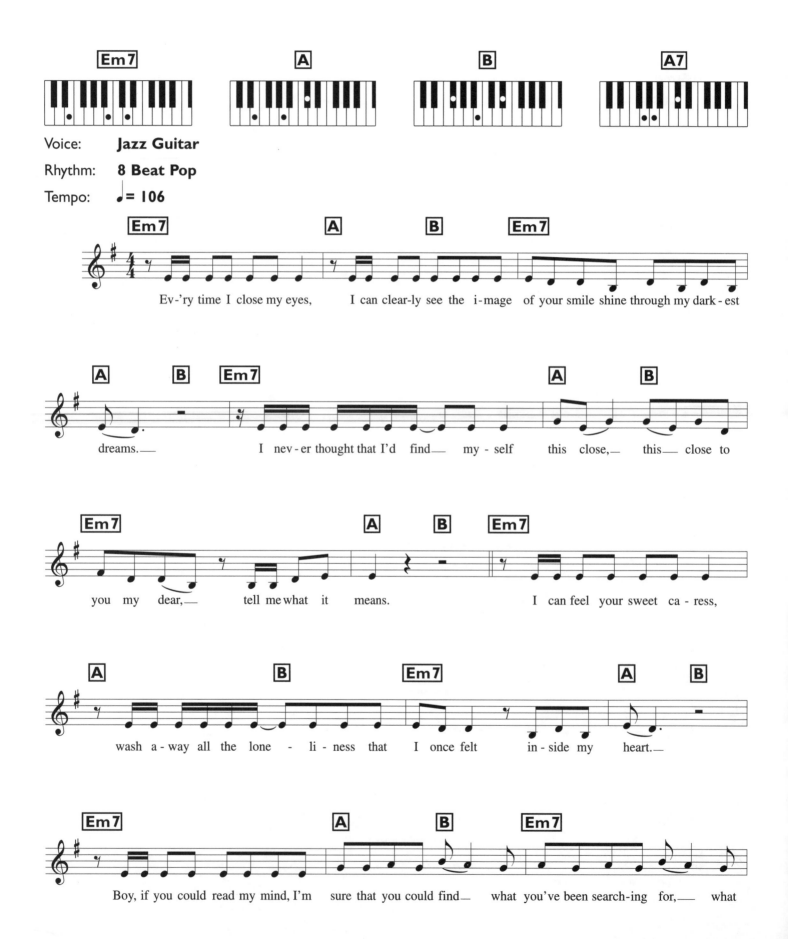

I'M GONNA GETCHA GOOD!

Words & Music by Shania Twain & Robert John "Mutt" Lange

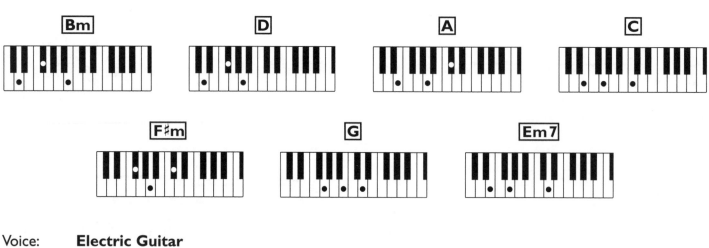

Voice: **Electric Guitar**

Rhythm: **Funky Pop 1**

Tempo: ♩ = 124

Don't want you for the week-end, don't want you for a night.

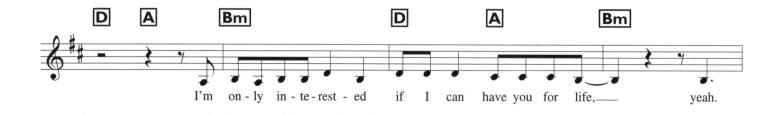

I'm on-ly in-te-rest-ed if I can have you for life,—— yeah.

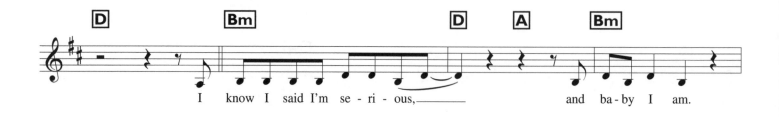

I know I said I'm se-ri-ous,—— and ba-by I am.

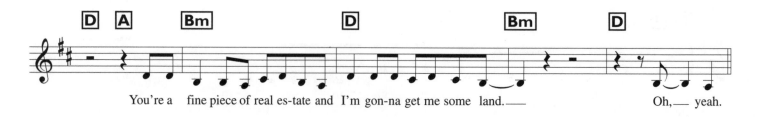

You're a fine piece of real es-tate and I'm gon-na get me some land.—— Oh,—— yeah.

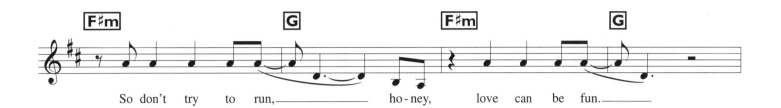

So don't try to run,————— ho-ney, love can be fun.—————

There's no need— to be a - lone— when you— find— that some - one.

I'm gon-na get-cha while I got-cha in— sight, I'm gon-na get-cha, if it takes all— night.—

You can bet-cha by the time I say— go, you'll nev - er say— no.—

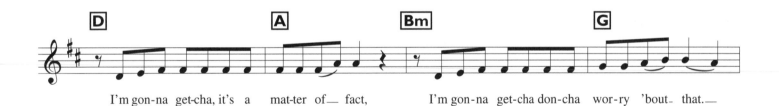

I'm gon-na get-cha, it's a mat-ter of— fact, I'm gon-na get-cha don-cha wor-ry 'bout_ that.—

You can bet your bot-tom dol - lar, in— time you're gon - na be— mine.— Just like I

should,— I'll get-cha good.— Oh,— I'm gon-na get-cha good.

Instrumental

IF YOU'RE NOT THE ONE

Words & Music by Daniel Bedingfield

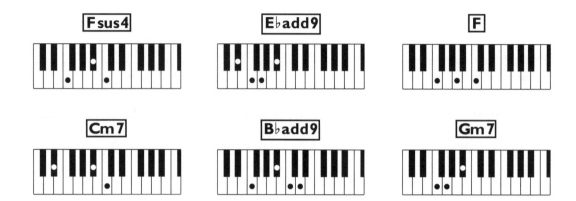

Voice: **Flute**

Rhythm: **Lite Pop**

Tempo: ♩ = 120

If you're not the one —— then why does ——

—— my soul —— feel —— glad —— to - day? —— If

you're not the one —— then why does —— my hand —— fit yours —— this way? —— If

you are not mine —— then why does —— your heart re - turn —— my call? —— If

you are not mine— would I have— the strength— to stand— at all?—

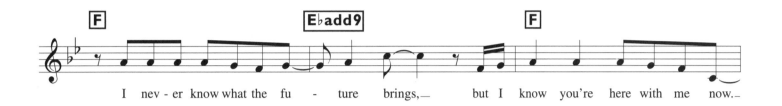

I nev - er know what the fu - ture brings,— but I know you're here with me now.—

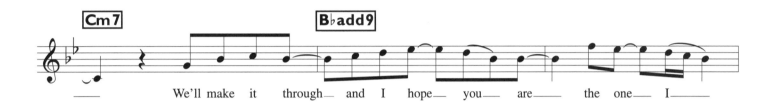

— We'll make it through— and I hope— you— are— the one— I—

share my— life— with.— I don't wan-na run a - way— but I—

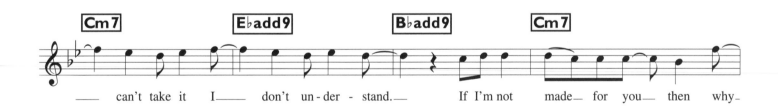

— can't take it I— don't un-der - stand.— If I'm not made— for you— then why—

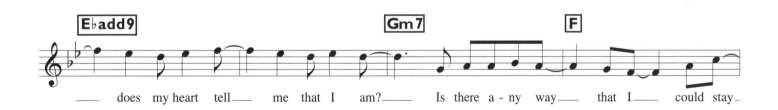

— does my heart tell— me that I am?— Is there a - ny way— that I— could stay—

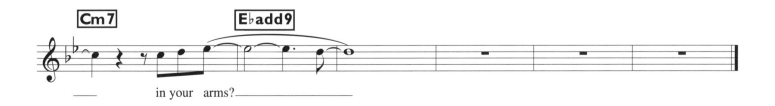

— in your arms?—

IN MY PLACE

Words & Music by Guy Berryman, Jon Buckland, Will Champion & Chris Martin

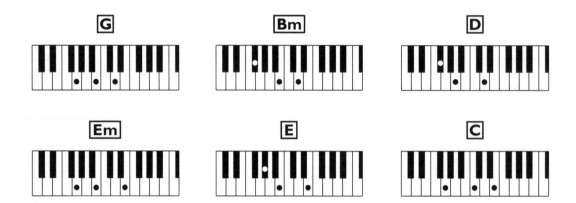

Voice: **Clarinet**

Rhythm: **Pop Rock 1**

Tempo: ♩ = 72

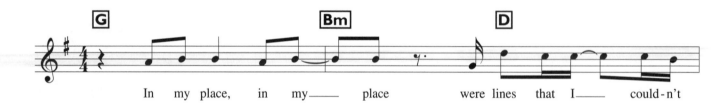

In my place, in my —— place were lines that I —— could-n't

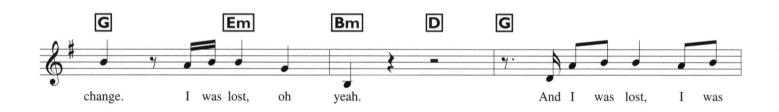

change. I was lost, oh yeah. And I was lost, I was

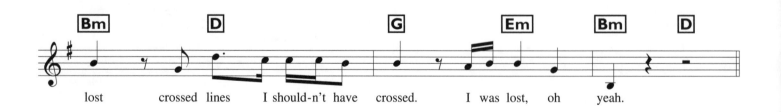

lost crossed lines I should-n't have crossed. I was lost, oh yeah.

Yeah, —— how long must — you wait for —— it? Yeah. — How

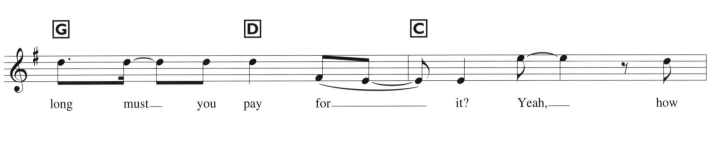

long   must—   you   pay   for——————   it?   Yeah,——   how

long   must—   you   wait   for——————   it?   Ah, for   it.   Sing-ing

please,   please,——   please——   come   back   and   sing   to

me,   to   me,   ah   me.——————   Come   on   and   sing   it

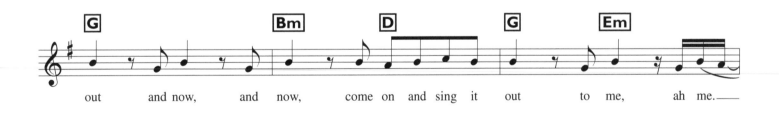

out   and now,   and   now,   come   on   and sing   it   out   to   me,   ah me.——

——   Come back and sing   to   me,   in my   place,   in my   place,   were   lines   that   I   could-n't

change   and   I   was   lost,   oh   yeah.——   Oh——   yeah.——————

THE KETCHUP SONG (ASEREJE)

Music & Lyrics by Francisco Manuel Ruiz Gomez

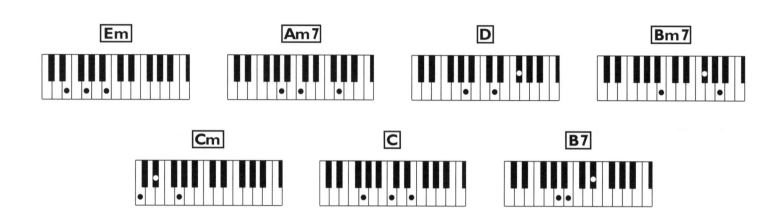

Voice: **Pearl Drop**

Rhythm: **Lambada**

Tempo: ♩ = 182

Fri - day night, it's par - ty time, feel - ing rea - dy, look - ing fine, Vie - ne die - go rum - be -

- an - do. With the ma - gic in his eyes, check - ing ev - 'ry girl in sight,

groov - ing like he does the mam - bo.— And he's the man a - lli en la dis - co, play - ing

sex - y, feel - ing hot - ter, he's the king, bail - an - do el rit - mo ra - ta - tang - a. And the

D. J. that he knows well, on the spot al-ways a - round twelve, plays the mix that Die - go mez-cla con la

sal - sa. Y la bai - la and he dan - ces y la can - ta_____ A - se - re -

- jé ja de jé de je - be tu de je - be - re se - i - bi - u - nou - va ma - ja - vi an de

bu - gui an de güi - di - di - pi.___ A - se - re - jé ja de jé de je - be tu de

je - be - re se - i - bi - u - nou - va ma - ja - vi an de bu - gui an de güi - di - di - pi.___

___ A - se - re - jé ja de jé de je - be tu de je - be - re se - i - bi - u - nou-

Repeat to fade

- va ma - ja - vi an de bu - gui an de güi - di - di - pi.___ A - se - re -

KISS KISS

Words & Music by Aksu Sezen, Juliette Jaimes & Steve Welton-Jaimes

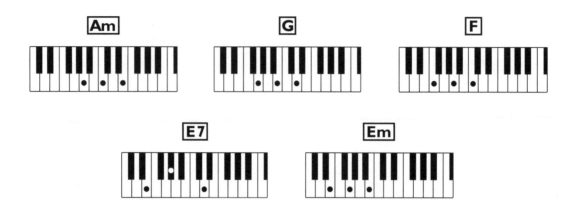

Voice: **Choir/Organ Layer**

Rhythm: **Funky Pop 1**

Tempo: ♩ = 98

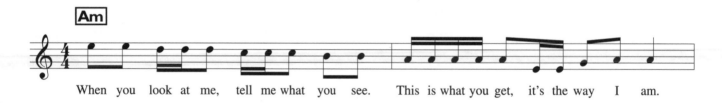

When you look at me, tell me what you see. This is what you get, it's the way I am.

When I look at you I wan-na be, I wan-na be some-where close to hea-ven with ne-an-der-thal man.

Don't go, I know you wan-na touch me, here, there and ev-'ry-where.

Sparks fly when we are to-geth-er, you can't de-ny the facts of life. You

LITTLE BY LITTLE

Words & Music by Noel Gallagher

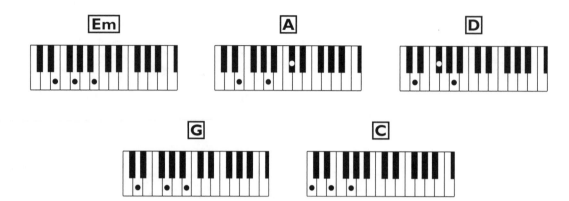

Voice: **Electric Piano**

Rhythm: **Pop Rock 1**

Tempo: ♩ = 74

We the peo - ple fight for our __ ex - is - tence. We

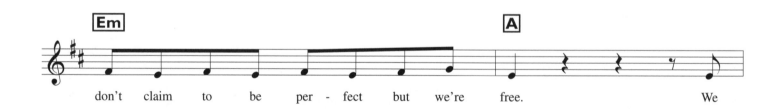

don't claim to be per - fect but we're free. We

dream our dreams __ a - lone with no __ re - sis - tance,

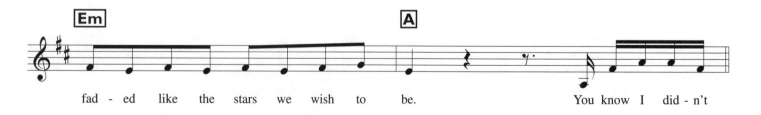

fad - ed like the stars we wish to be. You know I did - n't

A LITTLE LESS CONVERSATION

Words & Music by Billy Strange & Scott Davis

31

THE LONG AND WINDING ROAD

Words & Music by John Lennon & Paul McCartney

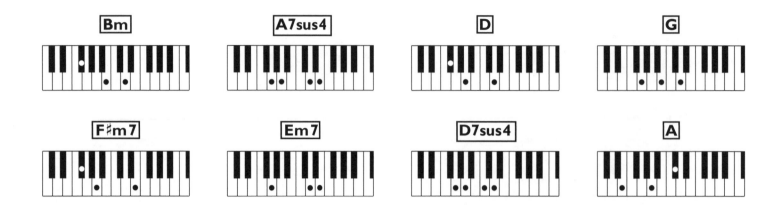

Voice: **Soprano Saxophone**

Rhythm: **Soul Ballad**

Tempo: ♩ = 70

The long and wind - ing road_____ that

leads to your door_____ will nev - er dis - ap -

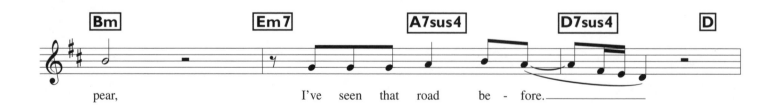

pear, I've seen that road be - fore._____

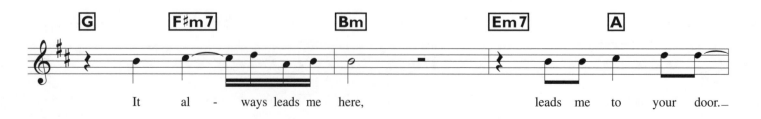

It al - ways leads me here, leads me to your door._

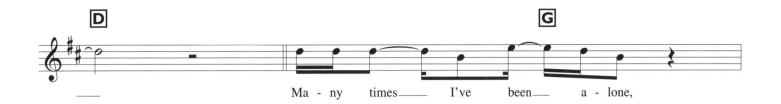

Ma - ny times___ I've been___ a - lone,

ma - ny times___ I've cried. Ooh a - ny - way___ you'll nev - er know___ the

ma - ny ways___ I've tried. But still they lead me back___ to that long___

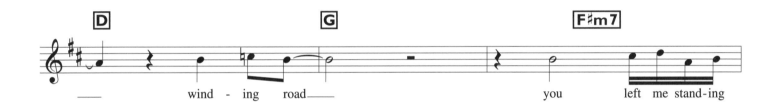

___ wind - ing road___ you left me stand-ing

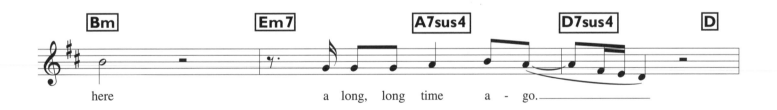

here a long, long time a - go.___

Don't leave___ me wait-ing here, lead me to your door.___

Yeah, yeah, yeah!

ONE LOVE

Words & Music by Mikkel SE, Hallgeir Rustan, Tor Erik Hermansen,
Simon Webbe, Antony Costa, Duncan James & Lee Ryan

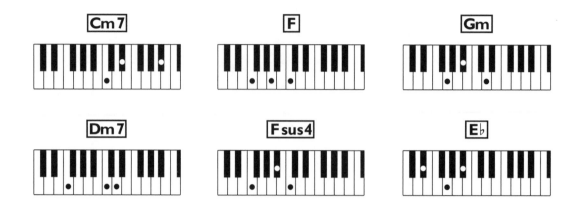

Voice: **Acoustic Guitar**

Rhythm: **Pop Ballad**

Tempo: ♩ = 94

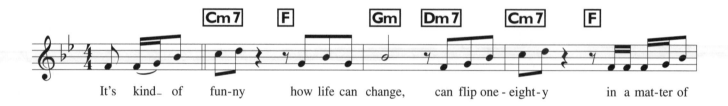

It's kind of fun-ny how life can change, can flip one-eight-y in a mat-ter of

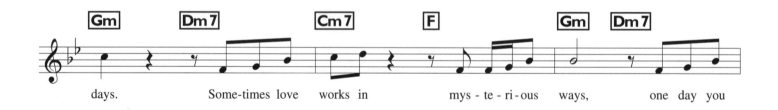

days. Some-times love works in mys-te-ri-ous ways, one day you

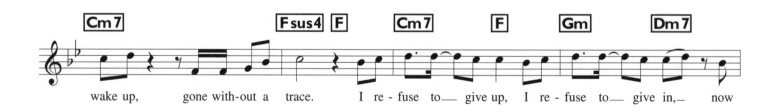

wake up, gone with-out a trace. I re-fuse to give up, I re-fuse to give in, now

you're my ev-'ry-thing. I don't wan-na give up, I don't wan-na give in, oh

ROUND ROUND

Words & Music by Brian Higgins, Keisha Buchanan, Mutya Buena, Heidi Range,
Florian Pflueger, Felix Stecher, Robin Hofmann & Rino Spadavecchiaand

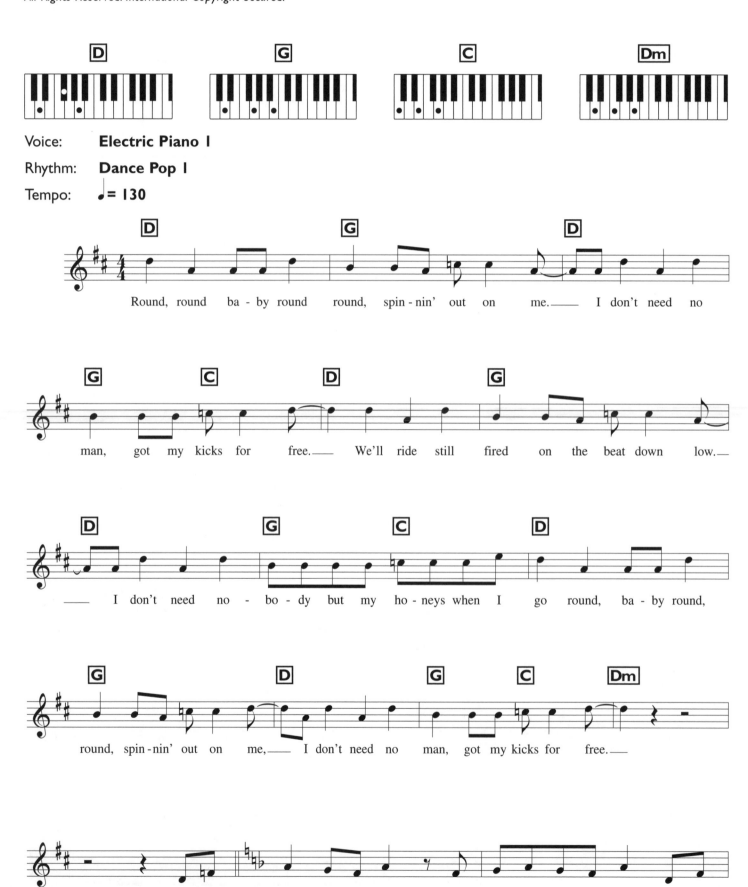

try to con-vince me then you bet-ter think a-gain. If you move to the mu-sic, the

mu-sic's got to give. If it's too com-pli-ca-ted, that's the way I wan-na live.

If you hate me, I will show— you how to brain me in-to some-thing new.

If you want me, run a-way— now; if you stop me, then I'll hit the ground.

Round, round ba-by round round, spin-nin' out on me.—

— I don't need no man, got my kicks for free.— We'll ride still

Repeat ad lib. to fade

fired on the beat down low.— I don't need no-bo-dy but my ho-neys when I

SACRED TRUST

Words & Music by Barry Gibb, Robin Gibb & Maurice Gibb

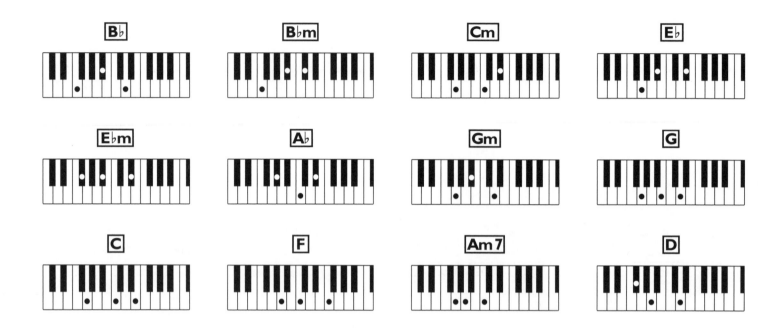

Voice: **Studio Piano**

Rhythm: **Dance Pop 2**

Tempo: ♩ = 110

I meant to fight it to the fi-nish but you made me for-get, I know it's

pos-si-ble I'm dream-ing, don't wake me yet. You know I love you, I can't see the day from night.

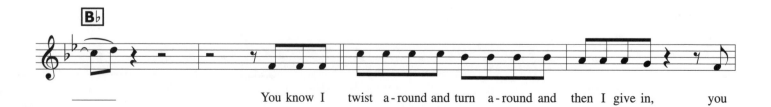

You know I twist a-round and turn a-round and then I give in, you

THE TIDE IS HIGH (GET THE FEELING)

Words & Music by John Holt, Howard Barrett, Tyrone Evans, Bill Padley & Jem Godfrey
© Copyright 1968 & 2002 The Sparta Florida Music Group Limited (85%)/
Wise Buddah Music Limited/Universal Music Publishing Limited (15%).
All Rights Reserved. International Copyright Secured.

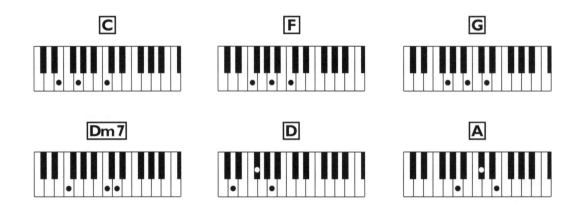

Voice: **Flute**

Rhythm: **Soft Rock 2**

Tempo: ♩ = 104

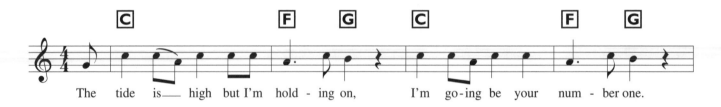

The tide is— high but I'm hold-ing on, I'm go-ing be your num-ber one.

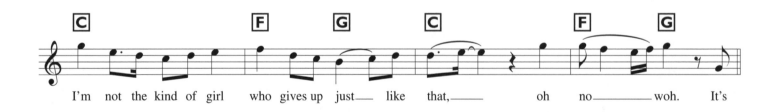

I'm not the kind of girl who gives up just— like that,—— oh no———woh. It's

not the things— you do that tease and hurt me—bad. But it's the way you do the things— you

do to me. I'm not the kind of girl— who gives up just— like that,—— oh

UNBREAKABLE

Words & Music by Jorgen Elofsson & John Reid

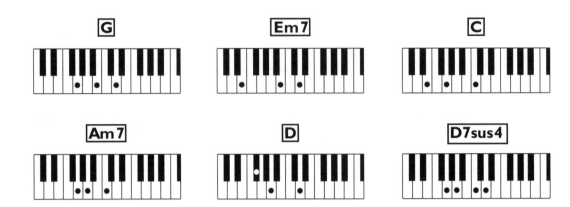

Voice: **Strings**

Rhythm: **Love Ballad**

Tempo: ♩ = 54

Took my hand, touched my heart,_____

held me close,___ you were al - ways there by my

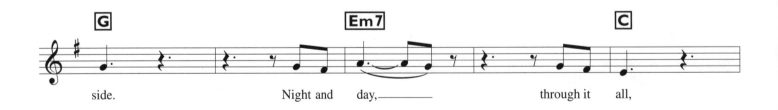

side. Night and day,_____ through it all,

ba - by, come what may.____ Swept a - way on a wave of e - mo-

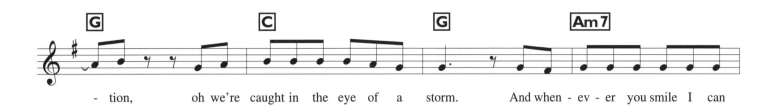

- tion, oh we're caught in the eye of a storm. And when - ev - er you smile I can

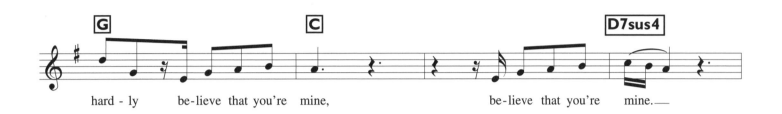

hard - ly be - lieve that you're mine, be - lieve that you're mine.——

This love is un - break - a - ble,—— it's un - mis - take - a - ble,——

and each time I look in your eyes—— I—— know why,

this love is un - touch - a - ble, I feel in my heart,—— just—— can't de -

- ny, each time I look in your eyes, oh ba - by, I know why,

this love is un - break - a - ble.

UNDERNEATH YOUR CLOTHES

Words by Shakira
Music by Shakira & Lester Mendez

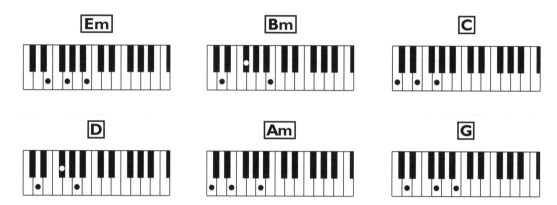

Voice: **Electric Piano 1**
Rhythm: **Pop Rock 2**
Tempo: ♩ = 84

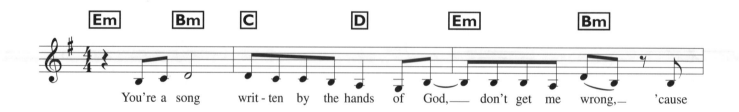

You're a song writ-ten by the hands of God,— don't get me wrong,— 'cause

this might sound to you a bit odd.— But you own the place,— where all my thoughts go

hid - ing and right un-der your clothes is where— I find them.—

Un - der - neath your clothes— there's an end-less sto - ry. There's the man I chose,

WHEREVER YOU WILL GO

Words & Music by Arron Kamin & Alex Band

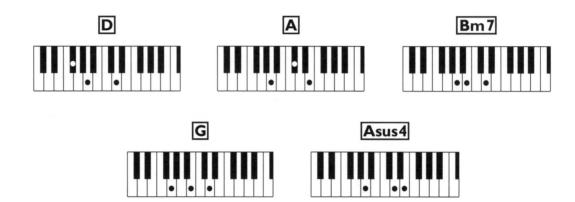

Voice: **Tenor Saxophone**

Rhythm: **Dance Pop 1**

Tempo: ♩ = 112

So late - ly, been wond - 'ring, who will_ be there_

_ to take_ my place,_ when I'm_ gone you'll need_ love

to light_ the sha - dows on_ your face._ If a great

_ wave_ shall fall_ it - 'll fall_ up - on_ us all.

Then bet - ween___ the sand___ and stone___ could you make

___ it on___ your own. If I___ could, then I___ would,

I'll go___ wher - ev - er you___ will go.___ Way up___ high

or down___ low, I'll go___ wher - ev - er you___ will go.___

___ I'll go wher -

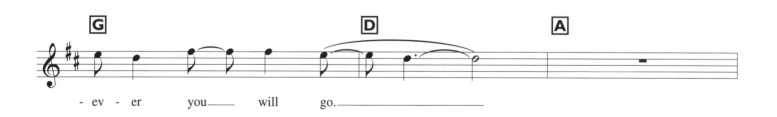

- ev - er you___ will go.___

7/04 (51770)

EASIEST KEYBOARD COLLECTION

Easy-to-play melody line arrangements for all keyboards with chord symbols and lyrics. Suggested registration, rhythm and tempo are included for each song together with keyboard diagrams showing left-hand chord voicings used.

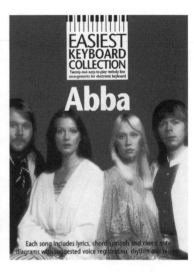

Showstoppers

Consider Yourself (Oliver!), Do You Hear The People Sing? (Les Misérables), I Know Him So Well (Chess), Maria (West Side Story), Smoke Gets In Your Eyes (Roberta) and 17 more big stage hits.
Order No. AM944218

Pop Classics

A Whiter Shade Of Pale (Procol Harum), Bridge Over Troubled Water (Simon & Garfunkel), Crocodile Rock (Elton John) and 19 more classic hit songs, including Hey Jude (The Beatles), Imagine (John Lennon), and Massachusetts (The Bee Gees).
Order No. AM944196

90s Hits

Over 20 of the greatest hits of the 1990s, including Always (Bon Jovi), Fields Of Gold (Sting), Have I Told You Lately (Rod Stewart), One Sweet Day (Mariah Carey), Say You'll Be There (Spice Girls), and Wonderwall (Oasis).
Order No. AM944229

Abba

A great collection of 22 Abba hit songs. Includes: Dancing Queen, Fernando, I Have A Dream, Mamma Mia, Super Trouper, Take A Chance On Me, Thank You For The Music, The Winner Takes It All, and Waterloo.
Order No. AM959860

Also available...